W9-APC-945

DATE DUE

NOV 1 3	FEB 1 8
NOV 3 0	
DEC 0 7	MAR 1 9
DEC 1 7	MAR 2 6
	APR 1 4
JAN 0 7	APR 2 3
JAN 1 4	MAY 0 4
	MAY 1 2
JAN 2 5	MAY 2 1
Jan 29	
FEB 1 2	

ONE SINGULAR SENSATION!

DUST OFF YOUR DANCING SHOES...

BECAUSE BABYMOUSE AND THE GANG...

ARE TAKING CENTER STAGE!

WILL BABYMOUSE GET THE LEAD IN THE MUSICAL? OR WILL FELICIA FURRYPAWS STEAL THE SHOW?

FIND OUT IN:

STARRING: BABYMOUSE!

(AS HERSELF)

MORE PRAISE FOR BABYMOUSE!

Sing your heart out for all the **BABYMOUSE** books:

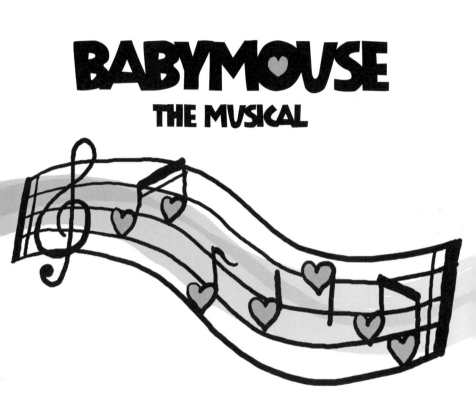

BABYMOUSE
THE MUSICAL

BY JENNIFER L. HOLM & MATTHEW HOLM

RANDOM HOUSE NEW YORK

Copyright © 2009 by Jennifer Holm and Matthew Holm.

All rights reserved.
Published in the United States by Random House Children's Books,
a division of Random House, Inc., New York.

Random House and colophon are registered trademarks of Random House, Inc.

Visit us on the Web!
www.randomhouse.com/kids
www.babymouse.com

Educators and librarians, for a variety of teaching tools, visit us at
www.randomhouse.com/teachers

Library of Congress Cataloging-in-Publication Data
Holm, Jennifer L.
Babymouse : the musical / by Jennifer & Matthew Holm.
   p.   cm.
Summary: As tryouts for the school musical begin, Babymouse takes the starring role in several imaginary Broadway productions, which also feature her debonair new classmate, Henry the Hedgehog.
ISBN 978-0-375-84388-4 (trade pbk.) — ISBN 978-0-375-93791-0 (lib. bdg.)
L Graphic novels. LL Graphic novels. 2. Musicals—Fiction. 3. Theater—Fiction.
4. Imagination—Fiction. 5. Mice—Fiction. 6. Animals—Fiction. 7. School—Fiction.]
I. Holm, Matthew. II. Title.
PZ7.7.H65Bal 2009 [Fic]—dc22 2008010891

MANUFACTURED IN MALAYSIA 12 11 10 9 8 7 6 5 4 3

One!

CLICK!

Singular sensation!

TAP
TAP
TAP

Every little book she reads.

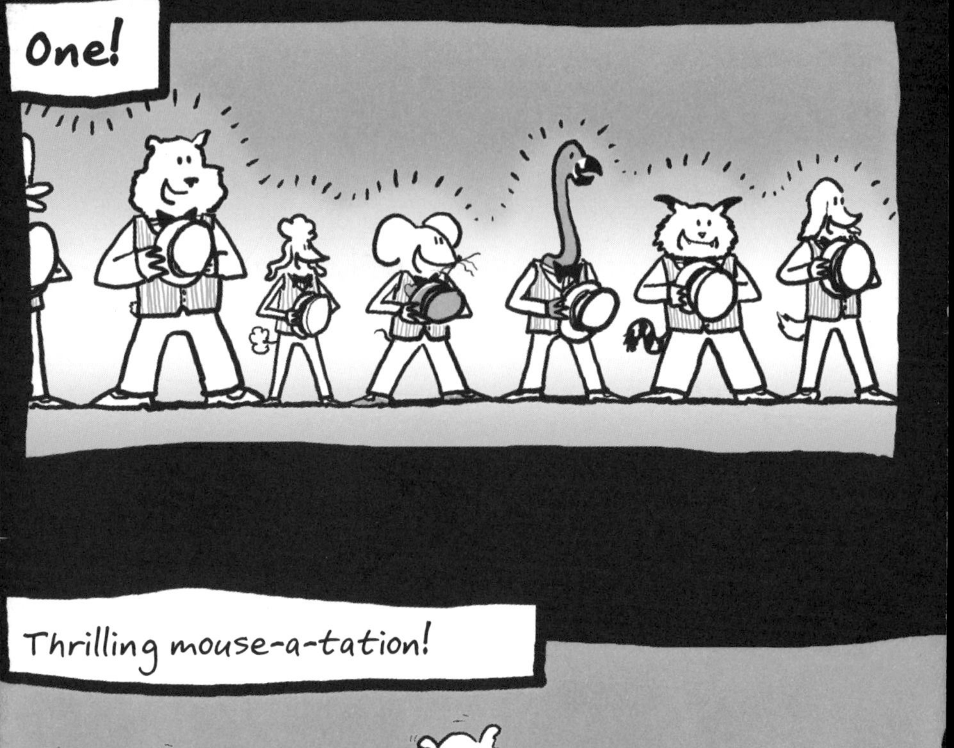
One!
Thrilling mouse-a-tation!
KICK!
KICK!
KICK!
KICK!

WOW. WHO KNEW THEY HAD CHANDELIERS DOWN HERE?

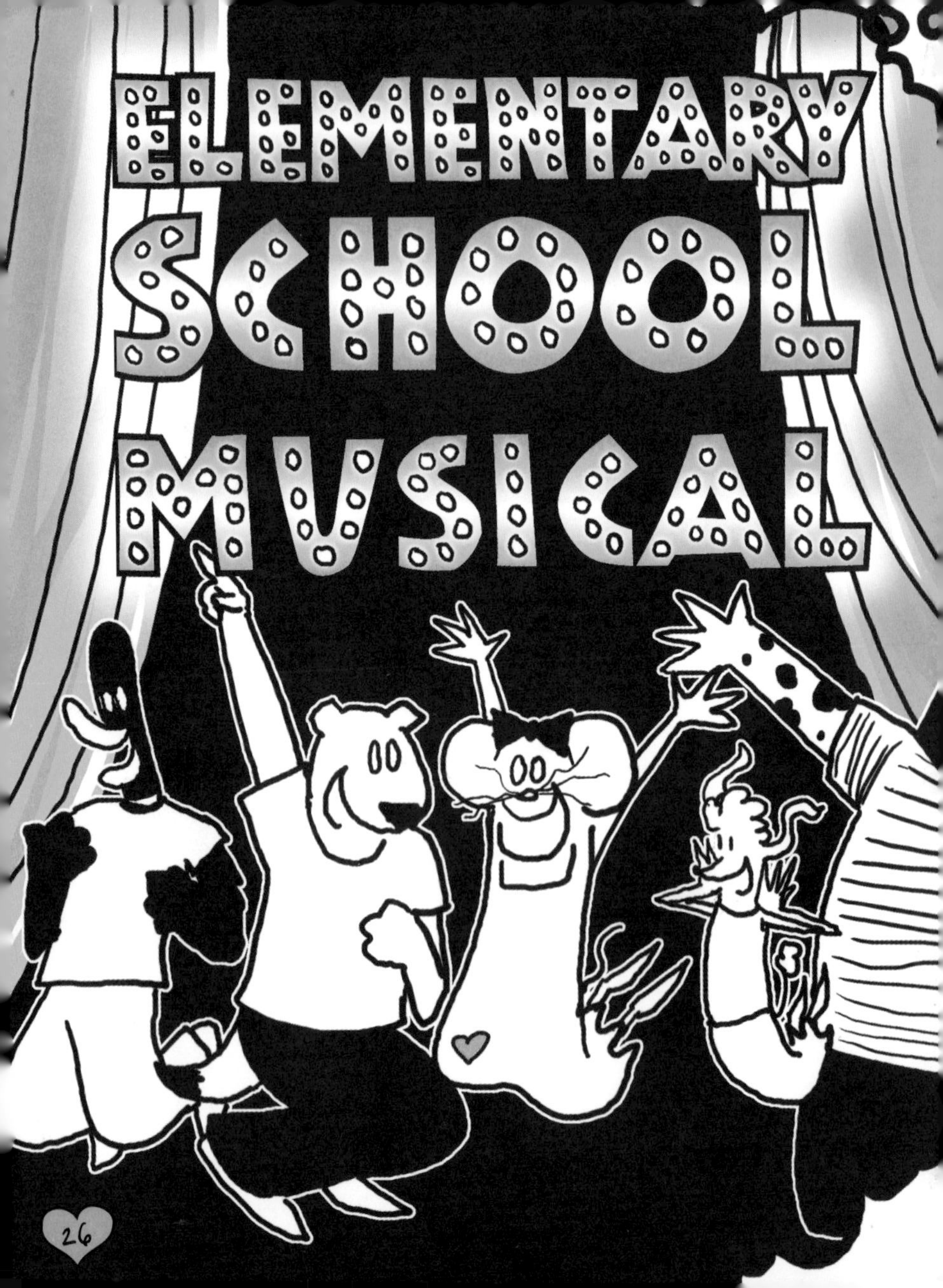
ELEMENTARY SCHOOL MUSICAL

TOM TOM TOM TOM TOM TOM
BRRRUUMMMMMMARU
TUM TOM TUM TA TOM TA
BRADA DA DA TOM
?

STEP STEP STEP STEP

UH, HI.

RABIES!

TOE FUNGUS!

DON'T HOLD YOUR BREATH, BABYMOUSE. I NEVER GET SICK.

BLINK!

CHEER UP, BABYMOUSE. MAYBE A HAIR BALL WILL GET STUCK IN HER THROAT.

SIGH.

43

CAN WE GET BACK TO THE STORY, PLEASE?

RYDELL HIGH SCHOOL

55

89

BABYMOUSE
CAPTION CONTEST WINNER!

BABYMOUSE, YOU ATE THOSE **FISH CUPCAKES** THAT WERE FOR FELICIA'S PARTY?

URP! I WISH YOU HAD WARNED ME FIRST!

OOG... I THINK I CAN STILL TASTE THEM....

THANKS AND CONGRATULATIONS TO THE AUTHOR OF OUR WINNING CAPTION, **CORAL JOHNSON** OF GALVESTON, TEXAS!